HUG A SLUG OR SNOG A FROG?

CHRIS P. BACON

RED FOX

HUG A SLUG OR SNOG A FROG?
A RED FOX BOOK 978 1 849 41868 3

First published in Great Britain by Red Fox,
an imprint of Random House Children's Publishers UK
A Random House Group Company

This edition published 2012

1 3 5 7 9 10 8 6 4 2

Text copyright © Random House Children's Publishers UK, 2012
Illustrations copyright © Nigel Baines, 2012

The Random House Group Limited supports the Forest Stewardship
Council (FSC®), the leading international forest certification organization.
Our books carrying the FSC label are printed on FSC®-certified paper.
FSC is the only forest certification scheme endorsed by the leading
environmental organizations, including Greenpeace.
Our paper procurement policy can be found at
www.randomhouse.co.uk/environment.

 Mixed Sources
Product group from well-managed
forests and other controlled sources
www.fsc.org Cert no. TT-COC-2139
© 1996 Forest Stewardship Council

RANDOM HOUSE CHILDREN'S PUBLISHERS UK
61–63 Uxbridge Road, London W5 5SA

www.**randomhousechildrens**.co.uk
www.**totallyrandombooks**.co.uk
www.**randomhouse**.co.uk

Addresses for companies within The Random House Group Limited
can be found at: www.randomhouse.co.uk/offices.htm

THE RANDOM HOUSE GROUP Limited Reg. No. 954009

A CIP catalogue record for this book is available from the British Library.

Printed and bound in Great Britain by Clays Ltd, St Ives plc

*With many thanks
to Mitchell Symons.*

BE KIDNAPPED BY NASTY CRIMINALS

OR

ABDUCTED BY KIND ALIENS?

IT'S A FACT!
Sanguinary ants raid the nests of other ant tribes, kill the queen and kidnap the workers.

IT'S A FACT!
Robert Louis Stevenson wrote most of *Kidnapped* in bed.

IT'S A FACT!
When scientists at Australia's Parkes Observatory began picking up radio waves, they thought they had proof of alien life. However, it turned out that the emissions came from a microwave in the building.

WOULD YOU RATHER...

LIVE ON A DIET OF BOGEYS AND ICE CREAM
OR
CHANGE YOUR NAME TO BOGEYS AND ICE CREAM?

IT'S A FACT! The European Patents Office say that the most commonly requested item among its thirty-one million patent documents is sardine-flavoured ice cream. A spokesman says, 'No one believes that it actually exists until they've called it up and seen it themselves.'

WOULD YOU RATHER...

BE BEST FRIENDS WITH THE INCREDIBLE HULK
OR
IRON MAN?

IT'S A FACT! Magnetic north is actually a thousand miles away from the north pole ('true north'). The north pole is technically located at 90°N (and any longitude) but magnetic north is currently at 73°N, 100°W.

JUST FOR FUN! What do you call a big green thing that sits in the corner and cries? The Incredible Sulk.

EAT STRAWBERRY-FLAVOURED DOG POO

OR

DOG POO-FLAVOURED STRAWBERRIES?

IT'S A FACT! In Belgium, there is a museum dedicated to strawberries (la Musée de la Fraise).

BE THE ONLY PERSON IN THE WORLD WITH AN IDENTICAL TWIN

OR

THE ONLY PERSON IN THE WORLD WITHOUT ONE?

IT'S A FACT!
Identical twins share the same DNA, but have their own fingerprints.

IT'S A FACT!
The secret language that many twins often have is called 'ideoglossia'.

WOULD YOU RATHER...

HAVE EYES MADE OF HAM
OR
EYES MADE OF CHEESE?

JUST FOR FUN! What sort of
cheese is made backwards?
Edam!

HAVE TO SPRINKLE ALL YOUR FOOD WITH SUPER-HOT CHILLI POWDER FOR THE REST OF YOUR LIFE — EVEN DESSERTS

OR

HAVE TO EAT A LARGE BOWLFUL OF MAGGOTS AND PUS, ONCE A YEAR?

IT'S A FACT! The hottest chilli in the world is the Trinidad Moruga. When a team of researchers was picking the spicy peppers, they each went through several pairs of rubber gloves because the chillis kept soaking through them!

WOULD YOU RATHER...

BE COLOUR BLIND OR TONE DEAF?

IT'S A FACT! Girls have more genes than boys, and because of this are better protected against things like colour blindness.

HAVE ONE EXTRA EYE OR TWO EXTRA ARMS?

IT'S A FACT! The tuatara lizard of New Zealand has three eyes – two that are positioned normally and an extra one on top of its head.

WOULD YOU RATHER...

PUT YOUR HAND INTO A NEST OF DEATHSTALKER SCORPIONS FOR ONE MINUTE

OR

BE IN A LOCKED ROOM WITH A BLACK MAMBA FOR FIVE MINUTES?

IT'S A FACT!

The deathstalker is responsible for about 75 per cent of scorpion-related deaths throughout the world.

IT'S A FACT!

The black mamba is an extremely aggressive snake, and will attack its victims without being provoked at all. It's named after the colour of the inside of its mouth – its scales are usually green or grey, not black.

GO WITHOUT CHIPS FOR THE REST OF YOUR LIFE

OR

ONLY BE ALLOWED TO EAT CHIPS FOR THE REST OF YOUR LIFE?

IT'S A FACT!

Every year enough potatoes are grown worldwide to cover a four-lane motorway circling the world six times.

IT'S A FACT!

In 1778 Prussia and Austria fought the Potato War in which each side tried to starve the other by consuming their potato crop.

WOULD YOU RATHER...

TRAVEL UP TO THE MOON
OR
DOWN TO THE MARIANA TRENCH?

IT'S A FACT! The deepest point on our planet is Challenger Deep in the Mariana Trench, where it's a staggering 11,033 metres below sea level.

IT'S A FACT! Fewer people have travelled deeper than two kilometres under the sea than have gone up to the moon!

BE A BEAR

OR

BE RULED

BY BEARS?

IT'S A FACT! There are eight species of bear, including polar bears, pandas and sloth bears. The smallest species of bear is the sun bear. Koalas are not bears, though – they're marsupials.

**BE SICK
THREE TIMES
ON YOUR
TEACHER
OR
HAVE TO
CLEAN
UP YOUR
TEACHER'S
SICK?**

IT'S A FACT! The Roman vomitoriums were not places where people could throw up after eating too much at banquets. In fact, they were passageways and tunnels in the great amphitheatres like the Colosseum that were there to make sure people weren't crushed on their way in or out. They were called vomitoriums because people were spewed out of the amphitheatres so quickly.

BE IN THE HARRY POTTER FILMS OR IN THE PIRATES OF THE CARIBBEAN FILMS?

IT'S A FACT! Pirates wore earrings in the belief that it improved their eyesight.

HAVE HAIR MADE OF
SOGGY SPAGHETTI
OR
A NOSE MADE OF PLASTICINE?

IT'S A FACT! 'The Spaghetti Harvest', a 'documentary' on the BBC TV programme *Panorama* in 1957, was probably the most famous British April Fools' Day prank of all time. Highly respected presenter Richard Dimbleby told the audience about the spaghetti harvest and showed them the spaghetti 'growing' and being 'dried' in the sun. Millions of people fell for it!

BE A BRILLIANT SUPERVILLAIN OR AN AVERAGE SUPERHERO?

IT'S A FACT! The first comic featuring Superman was published in 1938!

IT'S A FACT! Superman's arch-nemesis, Lex Luther, first appeared in 1940. Lex wasn't originally bald; the artist drawing him for 'Superman #10' made a mistake, and as it made him look more evil, DC Comics decided he should stay that way.

EAT BAKED BAT (A DISH FROM SAMOA) OR CRISPY ROASTED TERMITES (A DISH FROM SWAZILAND)?

IT'S A FACT! Bee grubs in coconut cream is a popular dish in Thailand, while stuffed bear's paw is a delicacy in Romania. Yum!

CARRY A ROTTEN APPLE CORE WITH YOU EVERYWHERE YOU GO

OR

REFUSE TO SIT IN ANY CHAIR UNTIL YOU HAVE JUMPED OVER IT SIX TIMES?

IT'S A FACT! In eighteenth-century America, apples were known as 'winter bananas'.

CELEBRATE YOUR BIRTHDAY ON THE VERY SAME DAY AS ONE OF YOUR BROTHERS OR SISTERS

OR

ON CHRISTMAS DAY?

IT'S A FACT! In the carol 'The Twelve Days of Christmas' the total number of gifts that 'my true love gave to me' is 364.

OWN THE REAL-LIFE ORANGE SET FROM THE GAME MONOPOLY (BOW STREET, MARLBOROUGH STREET AND VINE STREET) OR THE DARK BLUE SET (PARK LANE AND MAYFAIR)?

IT'S A FACT! More Monopoly money is printed in a year than real money throughout the world.

IT'S A FACT! In Monopoly, the most money you can lose in one trip round the board (going to jail only once) is £26,040. The most money you can lose in one turn is £5,070. If, on the other hand, no one ever buys anything, players could eventually break the bank.

WOULD YOU RATHER...

SAY 'THE SIXTH SICK SHEIK'S SIXTH SHEEP'S SICK'
OR
'A BIG BLACK BUG BIT A BIG BLACK BEAR, MADE THE BIG BLACK BEAR BLEED BLOOD'?

JUST FOR FUN! Other tongue-twisters include, 'If Stu chews shoes, should Stu choose the shoes he chews?' and 'Rory the warrior and Roger the worrier were wrongly reared in a rural brewery' – try challenging your friends to see who can say them faster!

WOULD YOU RATHER...

FIND OUT THE QUEEN IS REALLY YOUR MOTHER, BUT NEVER BE ALLOWED TO TELL ANYONE
OR
BE THE QUEEN FOR ONE WEEK?

IT'S A FACT! Queen Elizabeth II was the first member of the Royal Family ever to leave home for a haircut. It was in Malta, back in the days when she was a princess.

IT'S A FACT! She and Prince Philip were related before they married. They're third cousins (through their descent from Queen Victoria) and second cousins once removed (through King Christian IX of Denmark).

IT'S A FACT! The Queen is allowed to drive without taking a driving test, pardon any of the prisoners in her jails, and send letters without putting stamps on them!

HAVE YOUR OWN JET PACK OR YOUR OWN MINI SUBMARINE?

IT'S A FACT! In 1620, Dutch inventor Cornelius van Drebbel launched the world's first submarine in the Thames. The first military submarine – the Turtle – was built in 1775.

WOULD YOU RATHER...

NOT KNOW YOUR LEFT FROM YOUR RIGHT
OR
NOT BE ABLE TO TELL UP FROM DOWN?

IT'S A FACT! 'Stewardesses' is the longest word you can type on the left-hand side of a keyboard.

IT'S A FACT! The ancient Egyptians thought it was good luck to enter a house with your left foot first.

WOULD YOU RATHER...

SPEND A WHOLE SCHOOL DAY IN YOUR UNDERWEAR
OR
BE NAKED FOR ONE LESSON?

IT'S A FACT! The first National Underwear Day was held in New York in 2003.

THROW UP BANANA MILKSHAKE OR PEE FIZZY LEMONADE?

IT'S A FACT! In late-seventeenth-century Paris, lemonade became the world's first marketed soft drink.

BE BRUCE WAYNE WITH NO BATMAN ABILITIES OR BATMAN WITHOUT BEING BRUCE WAYNE?

IT'S A FACT!
Batman's first evil nemesis was the Catwoman, who used Batman's special style and skills to create her own persona.

IT'S A FACT!
Did you know that Batman was a father? In the original DC Comics, Bruce has a son named Damian with Talia al Ghul, the daughter of villain Ra's al Ghul.

SIT BEHIND A VERY TALL PERSON IN THE CINEMA
OR
NEXT TO SOMEONE EATING A STINKY EGG SANDWICH?

JUST FOR FUN! You might buy a bag of popcorn when you go to the cinema, but the Japanese enjoy fried squid pancakes or octopus kebabs, the Indonesians prefer dried cuttlefish, and the Koreans like to chew on roasted octopus tentacles – including the suckers!

HAVE A RAP BATTLE WITH DAVID CAMERON OR A PIE-EATING CONTEST WITH PRINCE WILLIAM?

IT'S A FACT! David Cameron and Prince William both went to school at Eton – though not at the same time!

IT'S A FACT! Cornish pasties – pies containing meat, potato, swede and onion – were given a special sealed edge to make them easier for tin miners to hold with dirty hands.

WOULD YOU RATHER...

WEAR A T-SHIRT TO SCHOOL THAT SAYS 'TEACHERS SUCK'
OR
ONE THAT SAYS 'PLEASE TAKE MY LUNCH MONEY'?

JUST FOR FUN! What do you get if you cross a vampire and a teacher? Lots of blood tests!

WOULD YOU RATHER...

BE CHASED BY A HORSE-SIZED DUCK OR A HERD OF DUCK-SIZED HORSES?

JUST FOR FUN! What do you get if you cross a duck with a stick of dynamite? A firequacker!

BE ABLE TO DEFY GRAVITY EVERY TIME YOU SAY 'THANK YOU' TO SOMEONE (BUT SUDDENLY LOSE THAT POWER IF THEY SAY 'YOU'RE WELCOME')

OR

BE ABLE TO SUMMON AN ARMY OF TINY SOLDIERS TO DO YOUR BIDDING EVERY TIME YOU SNEEZE (BUT GET ATTACKED BY THOSE SOLDIERS IF SOMEONE SAYS 'BLESS YOU')?

IT'S A FACT! When the Americans sent a man into space, they spent a million dollars developing a pen that could write upside down in zero gravity. The Russians used a pencil.

WOULD YOU RATHER...

STICK YOUR HAND IN AN ELEPHANT'S MOUTH
OR
UP A GOAT'S BUM?

IT'S A FACT! Mountain goats aren't really goats. They're actually small antelopes.

BE ABLE TO SELECT YOUR DREAMS BEFORE YOU GO TO SLEEP

OR

BE ABLE TO REPLAY THEM ON TV THE NEXT DAY?

IT'S A FACT! The colder the room you sleep in, the more likely you are to have a bad dream.

WEAR CLOTHES AND SHOES EVERY HOUR OF THE DAY AND NIGHT OR ALWAYS BE NAKED?

IT'S A FACT! Every year there's a naked bike ride around central London!

BE STUCK ON A DESERT ISLAND ON YOUR OWN OR WITH YOUR VERY WORST ENEMY?

IT'S A FACT! On the radio programme *Desert Island Discs*, celebrities can choose what luxury they'd take to a desert island. These include unlimited paper and a pen (J. K. Rowling), a yacht (George Clooney) and a mirror (Simon Cowell).

ALWAYS BE TWO HOURS EARLY FOR SCHOOL OR AN HOUR LATE?

WISE WORDS! 'He who opens a school door closes a prison.' (Victor Hugo)

WOULD YOU RATHER...

EAT A BAR OF SOAP
OR
DRINK A BOTTLE OF SHAMPOO?

IT'S A FACT! The word 'shampoo'
comes from the Hindu word 'champ',
meaning 'to massage'.

GO ON A ONE-THOUSAND-MILE CAR JOURNEY WITH YOUR MOST ANNOYING RELATIVE
OR
SPEND A DAY TRAPPED IN A CAVE WITH A SKUNK?

IT'S A FACT! Skunks protect themselves by giving off a pungent and foul odour that you can smell from a mile away. They have other means of protection too. They can withstand five times the amount of snake venom that would kill a rabbit.

BE GIVEN THE ULTIMATE WEDGIE OR HAVE YOUR HEAD SHOVED DOWN THE TOILET?

IT'S A FACT!

The most impossible item to flush down the toilet is a ping-pong ball.

BE GIVEN £1,000,000
OR
THREE WISHES (IN WHICH YOU CAN'T ASK FOR MONEY)?

JUST FOR FUN! Three friends are shipwrecked on a lonely desert island. Desperate for food and water, they are searching the beach when one of them finds a glass bottle washed up on the sand. When they uncork the bottle, they release a genie, who offers them three wishes. The first friend wishes to be taken to an elegant apartment in Paris, with his own personal chef. The genie snaps his fingers, and the man disappears. The second friend wishes to go to Hollywood, to the most famous restaurant in town. With a snap of the genie's fingers, he's gone too. The third man, now alone on the island, looks around and says, 'I'm lonely. I wish my friends were back.'

LICK WASHING-UP LIQUID OFF A CHOCOLATE BISCUIT

OR

HONEY OFF SOME STINGING NETTLES?

IT'S A FACT! A bee produces only one-twelfth of a teaspoon of honey in its life.

BE UNABLE TO SLEEP FOR A WEEK
OR
HAVE TO STAY IN BED
FOR A MONTH?

IT'S A FACT! The scientific term
for sleepwalking is somnambulism.
Sleepwalking can last from thirty seconds
to thirty minutes!

WOULD YOU RATHER...

PEE YOUR PANTS IN PUBLIC THREE TIMES
OR
POO YOUR PANTS IN PRIVATE ONCE?

IT'S A FACT! A thirteen-year-old boy in India produced winged beetles in his urine after hatching the eggs in his body.

BE FORCED TO TALK EVERY MINUTE OF THE DAY (THOUGH NOT AT NIGHT) OR NOT BE ALLOWED TO TALK AT ALL?

WISE WORDS! 'The best thing about animals is they don't talk much.' (Thornton Wilder)

HAVE THE POWER TO MAKE PEOPLE APPEAR (INCLUDING THE DEAD!) OR THE POWER TO MAKE PEOPLE DISAPPEAR?

IT'S A FACT! A team of British and American researchers has started work on creating a real-life invisibility cloak!

NEVER BE ABLE TO USE A COMPUTER AGAIN

OR

NEVER BE ABLE TO SEE A REFLECTION OF YOURSELF IN A MIRROR?

IT'S A FACT! A chimpanzee can learn to recognize itself in a mirror, but a monkey can't.

ENDURE A CAR ALARM OUTSIDE YOUR WINDOW ALL NIGHT OR BE WOKEN BY YOUR FRIEND WITH A CHINESE BURN?

IT'S A FACT! The term 'Chinese burn' comes from Chinese martial arts, because when you throw an opponent over and hold onto their arms it often leaves a burn mark.

WOULD YOU RATHER...

HAVE BABY PHOTOS OF YOURSELF PUT ONLINE
OR
HAVE A FRONT TOOTH PULLED OUT?

JUST FOR FUN! A woman gets on a bus with her baby. The bus driver says, 'Ugh, that's the ugliest baby I've ever seen!' The woman walks to the back of the bus and sits down, fuming. She says to a man next to her, 'The driver just insulted me!' The man says, 'You go up there and tell him off. Go on, I'll hold your monkey for you.'

WOULD YOU RATHER...

EAT NOTHING BUT CHEESE FOR A YEAR (ANY KIND)
OR
NOTHING BUT PRAWN COCKTAIL CRISPS?

JUST FOR FUN! How should you handle a dangerous cheese? Caerphilly.

BE ABLE TO FART THE NATIONAL ANTHEM
OR
CHANGE THE NATIONAL ANTHEM TO SOMEONE FARTING?

IT'S A FACT! If you farted continuously for six years and nine months, enough wind would be produced to equal the energy of an atomic bomb.

IT'S A FACT! The national anthem of Greece is 158 verses long.

HAVE THE FACE OF A BABY AND THE MIND OF AN OLD MAN

OR

THE FACE OF AN OLD MAN AND THE MIND OF A BABY?

IT'S A FACT!
A newborn baby's heart beats twice as fast as an adult's.

IT'S A FACT!
A newborn baby cries, on average, for 113 minutes a day.

NEVER BE ABLE TO TELL A LIE
OR
NEVER KNOW WHEN SOMEONE IS LYING TO YOU?

WISE WORDS!
'A lie told often enough becomes the truth.' (Lenin)

WISE WORDS!
'A lie can travel halfway around the world while the truth is putting on its shoes.' (Mark Twain)

PLAY FOOTBALL PROFESSIONALLY OR HAVE A SEASON TICKET FOR THE REST OF YOUR LIFE?

IT'S A FACT! Hull City is the only British football team that hasn't got any letters you can fill in with a pen.

WOULD YOU RATHER...

EAT THE WORLD'S SPICIEST CURRY
OR
THE WORLD'S BIGGEST
PORTION OF CHIPS?

IT'S A FACT! Britain's first Indian restaurant was opened more than fifty years before the first fish and chip restaurant.

GO FOR TWO WEEKS WITHOUT A BATH

OR

ONE WEEK WITHOUT BRUSHING YOUR TEETH?

IT'S A FACT!
Brushing your teeth with the water on wastes almost twenty litres of water.

IT'S A FACT!
Louis XIV of France took just three baths in his lifetime (and he had to be forced into taking those).

WOULD YOU RATHER...

HAVE A FOOTBALL FOR A HEAD
OR
A CRICKET BALL?

IT'S A FACT! The Marylebone Cricket Club used to represent England in overseas cricket matches. It was due to play its first overseas fixture in 1789 against France, but the French Revolution began, and that got in the way. Two hundred years later, in 1989, they finally played the game. The French won by seven wickets.

DIE INSTANTLY (AND PAINLESSLY) OR TAKE A LONG TIME TO DIE (BUT BE ABLE TO SAY YOUR GOODBYES)?

JUST FOR FUN! Before she was beheaded, Queen of France Marie Antoinette's final words were, 'Sir, I beg your pardon!' (She stepped on the executioner's foot as she walked to the guillotine.)

SHARE YOUR BEDROOM WITH SOMEONE WHO SNORES ALL THE TIME OR SOMEONE WHO FARTS ALL THE TIME?

JUST FOR FUN! I went to the doctor the other day and I said, 'Have you got anything for wind?' He gave me a kite.

WIN A GAME BY CHEATING

OR

LOSE IT FAIR AND SQUARE?

WISE WORDS! 'A thing worth having is a thing worth cheating for.' (W. C. Fields)

WISE WORDS! 'The first and worst of all frauds is to cheat oneself.' (Pearl Bailey)

POO THROUGH YOUR NOSE

OR

BE SICK OUT OF YOUR EAR?

IT'S A FACT!
People who live in the city have longer, thicker nose hairs than people who live in the country (because they breathe more polluted air).

IT'S A FACT!
When Sir Michael Caine was a child, his mother pasted his ears to his head to stop them sticking out.

BE A BRILLIANT CONCERT PIANIST OR WIN BRITAIN'S GOT TALENT?

IT'S A FACT! The piano covers the full spectrum of all orchestral instruments, from below the lowest note of the double bassoon to above the highest note of the piccolo.

HAVE TO WATCH YOUR MUM DO KARAOKE ON HOLIDAY

OR

YOUR DAD GO TO A NUDIST BEACH (AND ALL YOUR FRIENDS KNOW ABOUT IT)?

IT'S A FACT! A boat carrying sixty passengers capsized in Texas after it passed a nudist beach and everyone rushed to one side to have a closer look.

BE THE SUBJECT OF GOSSIP OR NEVER TALKED ABOUT?

IT'S A FACT! Trivia was a Roman goddess to whom sacrifices were offered at crossroads. Because travellers often engaged in idle gossip at crossroads, Trivia's name (referring to three roads coming together) came to be associated with the sort of information exchanged in such places.

BE GIVEN £100,000 BUT HAVE TO SPEND IT ALL ON THE MOST BORING SCHOOL UNIFORM EVER

OR

BE GIVEN £50 TO SPEND ON WHATEVER YOU LIKED?

WISE WORDS! 'Whoever said money can't buy happiness simply didn't know where to go shopping.' (Bo Derek)

WOULD YOU RATHER...

ONLY BE ABLE TO WHISPER
OR
ONLY BE ABLE TO SHOUT?

IT'S A FACT! Whispering wears out your voice more than a normal speaking tone. Whispering and shouting both stretch the vocal cords.

TRAVEL THREE HUNDRED YEARS BACK IN TIME AND BE KING OR QUEEN OF ENGLAND UNTIL THE AGE OF FORTY, THEN BE HANGED

OR

BE A LOYAL SERVANT, AND DIE PEACEFULLY (BUT POOR) AT NINETY?

IT'S A FACT! In 1679, three people named Green, Berry and Hill were hanged at Tyburn for a murder they committed on . . . Greenberry Hill.

THERE WERE NO ROADS IN THE WHOLE WORLD OR NO GRASS?

IT'S A FACT! A huge 10 per cent of the salt mined in the world each year is used to de-ice the roads in America.

HAVE THE ABILITY TO ERASE ANYTHING YOU SAID OR ANYTHING ANYONE ELSE SAID?

IT'S A FACT! The French expression 'Fait accompli' means something that has already happened and so can't be undone. We use it in English, too.

WOULD YOU RATHER...

EAT A BOWL OF ZOMBIE SNOT
OR
THE CONTENTS OF A WITCH'S
CAULDRON – WITHOUT CHECKING
WHAT'S INSIDE FIRST?

JUST FOR FUN! Two zombies are about to have a wrestling match. One says to the other, 'Do you want a piece of me?'

WOULD YOU RATHER...
MEET A MERMAID
OR
A MARTIAN?

IT'S A FACT! The number of UFO sightings reported increases when Mars is nearest to Earth.

TELL YOUR MUM A TERRIBLE LIE OR HAVE YOUR MUM LIE TO YOU?

WISE WORDS! 'Liars, when they speak the truth, are not believed.' (Aristotle)

WISE WORDS! 'It is always the best policy to speak the truth – unless, of course, you are an exceptionally good liar.' (Jerome K. Jerome)

BE A CIRCUS CLOWN OR AN ACROBAT?

IT'S A FACT! Students from all over the world go to Montreal in Canada to learn to be acrobats, trapeze artists, dancers and actors at the École Nationale du Cirque. This circus school works closely with the world famous Cirque du Soleil.

ONLY EVER BE ABLE TO EAT CEREAL (INCLUDING PORRIDGE) OR TOAST?

IT'S A FACT! The first ready-to-eat breakfast cereal was Shredded Wheat in 1893 (it beat Kellogg's Corn Flakes by just five years).

HAVE J. K. ROWLING DO YOUR ENGLISH HOMEWORK

OR

STEPHEN HAWKING DO YOUR MATHS HOMEWORK?

IT'S A FACT! J. K. Rowling and Harry Potter share a birthday – 31 July. The author has said that if she could transform into any animal, it would be an otter – the shape of Hermione's Patronus.

HAVE WRITTEN THE PIANO TUNE 'CHOPSTICKS' OR COMPOSED A BRILLIANT (BUT UNKNOWN) SYMPHONY?

IT'S A FACT! The song 'Chopsticks' was written in 1877 by Euphemia Allen, aged sixteen. She said that the correct way to play it was to chop the keys with the hands turned sideways.

OWN EVERY GADGET EVER INVENTED BY APPLE

OR

BY SONY?

IT'S A FACT! The first personal computer, the Apple II, went on sale in 1977.

WOULD YOU RATHER...

HAVE AN ENDLESS RUNNY NOSE
OR
ENDLESS DIARRHOEA?

IT'S A FACT! The world record for the longest sneezing spell is 977 days. Doctors estimate that this is over one million sneezes. Bless you!

BRUSH YOUR TEETH ONCE A DAY FOR TWENTY-FIVE MINUTES

OR

ONCE A WEEK FOR THIRTY SECONDS?

IT'S A FACT! The first toothbrush was invented in China in 1498.

EAT AN ICE-COLD LOLLY IN ONE GO

OR

DRINK A CUP OF BOILING HOT COFFEE IN ONE GULP?

IT'S A FACT! The first ice lolly dates back to 1923 when lemonade salesman Frank Epperson left a glass of lemonade with a spoon in it on a windowsill one very cold night. The next morning, the ice lolly was born!

WOULD YOU RATHER...

ALWAYS HAVE TO TELL THE TRUTH OR ALWAYS HAVE TO PERFORM ANY DARE?

WISE WORDS! 'Any fool can tell the truth, but it requires a man of some sense to know how to lie well.' (Samuel Butler)

HAVE X-RAY GLASSES OR JET BOOTS THAT ALLOWED YOU TO WALK UP WALLS?

IT'S A FACT! Spectacles were first worn in Italy in about 1285.

HAVE DAVID BECKHAM AS YOUR DAD OR JAMIE OLIVER?

IT'S A FACT! David Beckham's father was a kitchen fitter; Jamie Oliver's father ran a pub (where his son first learned to cook).

BE STUCK INDOORS ON THE SUNNIEST DAY OF THE YEAR
OR
STRANDED OUTSIDE ON THE RAINIEST?

IT'S A FACT! In 1986, a judge in California named Samuel King was annoyed that some jurors were absent from his court because of heavy rain, so he announced, 'I hereby order that it cease raining by Tuesday.' California then suffered a five-year drought. So in 1991 the judge decreed, 'Rain shall fall in California beginning on February 27th.' Later that day, California had its heaviest rainfall in a decade.

WOULD YOU RATHER...

EAT TEN GRAMS OF SOMEONE ELSE'S BOGEYS
OR
ONE HUNDRED GRAMS OF YOUR OWN EARWAX?

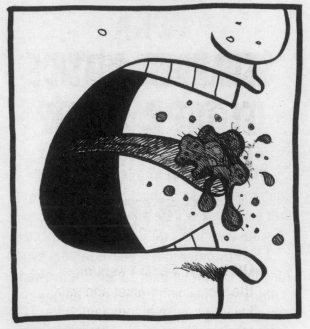

IT'S A FACT! Mucophagy is the medical term for eating your own snot.

BANG YOUR FUNNY BONE THREE TIMES OR GET A SURPRISE STATIC ELECTRIC SHOCK FROM A SHOPPING TROLLEY?

JUST FOR FUN! I went down to the local supermarket and said, 'I want to make a complaint, this vinegar's got lumps in it.' They told me, 'Those are pickled onions.'

SWIM A MILE IN VERY HOT WATER

OR

VERY COLD WATER?

IT'S A FACT! Every year on Christmas Day, people take a dip in the freezing Serpentine in London's Hyde Park. The first one took place in 1864.

PICK UP A TARANTULA IN YOUR BARE HANDS

OR

LET A SNAIL CRAWL ACROSS YOUR FACE?

IT'S A FACT!
The average garden snail has a top speed of 0.03 miles per hour.

IT'S A FACT!
Relative to its size, the ordinary house spider is eight times faster than an Olympic sprinter.

HAVE AMANDA HOLDEN AS OUR QUEEN

OR

DAVID WALLIAMS AS OUR PRIME MINISTER?

IT'S A FACT! Amanda Holden
likes to do crochet.

EAT NOTHING BUT SALT-AND-VINEGAR CRISPS FOR A YEAR

OR

NOTHING BUT CHOCOLATE-CHIP ICE CREAM?

IT'S A FACT! Children have more taste buds than adults.

IT'S A FACT! Over a twelve-day period, your body generates a whole new set of taste buds.

WOULD YOU RATHER...

CHANGE THE CURRENCY TO MONOPOLY MONEY
OR
TO BALLS OF BELLY-BUTTON FLUFF?

IT'S A FACT! The Monopoly square most often landed on is Trafalgar Square, followed by Go and then Marylebone Station.

EAT A SPOONFUL OF GARDEN SOIL (COMPLETE WITH WORMS) OR LICK A PUBLIC TELEPHONE?

IT'S A FACT! There are over 34,000 different types of worm.

IT'S A FACT! Worms have a special survival ability. If you accidentally cut a worm in half (don't try it, of course!) only half will die. The piece with the saddle (the fattest part of the body) will live.

GIVE UP SLEEP FOR A WEEK OR FOOD FOR A WEEK?

IT'S A FACT!
Humans are the only animals to sleep on their backs.

IT'S A FACT!
A person will die from a total lack of sleep more quickly than they will from starvation.

DRINK COKE
OR
PEPSI?

IT'S A FACT!

Diet Coke was invented in 1982. However, in 1379, a Mr and Mrs Coke of Yorkshire named their daughter 'Diot' (a short form of Dionisia, the modern-day name Denise).

IT'S A FACT!

Pepsi was created by Caleb Bradham in 1902 from a mixture of oil, spices, vanilla, sugar and an enzyme called pepsin.

SUCK A WHOLE STRAND OF COOKED SPAGHETTI THROUGH YOUR NOSE
OR
HAVE A PINCH OF PEPPER PUT INTO YOUR EAR?

IT'S A FACT! Pepper was highly prized in Elizabethan times, and was sold in individual grains.

CYCLE THREE MILES UP A VERY STEEP HILL

OR

TRAVEL ONE MILE DOWN A VERY STEEP HILL, SITTING IN THE BACK OF A SUPERMARKET TROLLEY?

IT'S A FACT! A French man named Michel Lotito ate 128 bicycles – as well as fifteen supermarket trolleys, six chandeliers, two beds and a pair of skis. (Don't try this at home!)

HAVE THREE HOURS OF PRIVATE DETENTION
OR
HAVE TO WRITE 'I AM A SILLY SAUSAGE' FIFTY TIMES ON THE BLACKBOARD IN FRONT OF YOUR WHOLE CLASS?

IT'S A FACT! The actor Jack Nicholson was in detention every day for a whole school year.

EVERYONE THOUGHT YOU WERE AN IDIOT OR A REALLY NASTY PERSON?

WISE WORDS! 'Never argue with an idiot. Bystanders can't tell the difference.' (Proverb)

BE BURIED ALIVE

OR

SHOT DEAD QUICKLY?

IT'S A FACT! In the 1500s, one out of twenty-five coffins was found to have scratch marks on the inside.

WOULD YOU RATHER...

BE SPIDER-MAN WITH A FEAR OF HEIGHTS
OR
BATMAN WITH A BROKEN ARM?

IT'S A FACT! There are people who claim that it's illegal to dress up as Batman in Australia. This is because of an obscure law which prohibits the wearing of dark clothes all over the body for fear that someone will look like a cat burglar.

BE CHASED BY AN ANGRY HIPPO OR A HUNGRY CROCODILE?

IT'S A FACT! A hippo can bite a crocodile in half.

IT'S A FACT! A hippo can outrun a man!

BE IN A PUBLIC TOILET AND REALIZE THERE'S NO TOILET PAPER
OR
DISCOVER IT DOESN'T FLUSH?

IT'S A FACT! The first time women and men used separate toilets was in 1739 at a Paris ball.

BE A CAT
OR
A DOG?

IT'S A FACT!
Cats have over one hundred vocal sounds; dogs have about ten.

WISE WORDS!
'Cats are smarter than dogs. You can't get eight cats to pull a sled through snow.' (Jeff Valdez)

SHAVE OFF YOUR EYEBROWS

OR

PLUCK OUT YOUR EYELASHES?

IT'S A FACT!
In Brazil, there's a species of cockroach that eats the eyelashes of young children while they're asleep.

IT'S A FACT!
In ancient Egypt, priests plucked every hair from their bodies, including their eyebrows and eyelashes.

DRINK A GLASS OF A STRANGER'S SALIVA

OR

HALF A GLASS OF TOILET WATER (AFTER YOUR DAD'S JUST BEEN TO THE TOILET)?

IT'S A FACT! Everyone sprays microscopic saliva droplets into the air when they talk – about two or three droplets for each word.

WOULD YOU RATHER...

NEVER USE YOUR PHONE AGAIN

OR

NEVER WATCH TV AGAIN?

IT'S A FACT! In the course of a lifetime, we spend about two years on the phone, and eat about 35,000 biscuits (not necessarily at the same time!).

KNOW THE PRECISE DATE OF YOUR DEATH
OR
THE PRECISE CAUSE OF YOUR DEATH?

WISE WORDS! 'On the plus side, death is one of the few things that can be done just as easily lying down.' (Woody Allen)

BE BART SIMPSON OR LISA?

IT'S A FACT! The characters of Homer, Marge, Lisa and Maggie were given the same first names as *Simpsons* creator Matt Groening's real-life father, mother and two sisters.

IT'S A FACT! Matt Groening incorporated his initials into the drawing of Homer; there's an M in his hair and his ear is the letter G.

HUG A SLUG OR SNOG A FROG?

IT'S A FACT! Frogs don't drink water –
they absorb it through their skin.

IT'S A FACT! The name for a group
of frogs is 'an army of frogs'
(but for toads, it's 'a knot of toads').

TAKE PART IN THE WORLD SCREAMING CHAMPIONSHIP (IN POLAND) OR THE WORLD MOSQUITO-KILLING CHAMPIONSHIP (IN FINLAND)?

JUST FOR FUN! Other unusual competitions include the World Nettle-Eating Championship, the World Walking-the-Plank Championship and the World Pea-Throwing Competition!

HAVE YOUR OWN PRIVATE JET BUT BE AFRAID OF FLYING

OR

A LUXURY YACHT BUT GET SEASICK?

IT'S A FACT! Admiral Lord Nelson, one of the most famous sea captains in history, was terribly seasick on every voyage of his life.

WOULD YOU RATHER...
LIVE IN FIFTY-DEGREE HEAT
OR
MINUS-FIFTY-DEGREE COLD?

IT'S A FACT! At minus fifty degrees your breath will freeze in mid-air and fall to the ground.

WOULD YOU RATHER...

LOSE YOUR SENSE OF TASTE FOR EVER OR YOUR SENSE OF SMELL?

IT'S A FACT! Girls can detect smell better than boys.

BE ATTACKED BY A SWARM OF ANGRY BEES OR A SINGLE DEADLY SNAKE?

IT'S A FACT! More people are killed each year by bees than by snakes.

IT'S A FACT! The Inland Taipan is the world's most poisonous snake. The venom it produces in one bite would be enough to kill two hundred thousand mice.

IT'S A FACT! A python can swallow a pig whole!

NEVER RECEIVE BIRTHDAY PRESENTS EVER AGAIN

OR

GET THE SAME PAIR OF BORING GREY SOCKS EVERY YEAR AS YOUR ONLY CHRISTMAS PRESENT?

IT'S A FACT! Between 1642 and 1652, Christmas was officially abolished by the Puritans. Imagine if Christmas was illegal nowadays!

HAVE A BATH IN COOKING OIL OR A BATH IN VINEGAR?

IT'S A FACT! Olive oil was once used for washing the body in Mediterranean countries.

WOULD YOU RATHER...

HAVE MOULDY CABBAGE LEAVES FOR EARS
OR
HAVE YOUR NOSE CUT OFF EVERY DAY, FOR IT TO GROW BACK PAINFULLY OVERNIGHT?

IT'S A FACT! In ancient China, the nose of a criminal who attacked travellers would be cut off as a punishment.

WOULD YOU RATHER...

EAT A BAR OF MILK CHOCOLATE AT EVERY MEAL (AND BECOME ENORMOUS!)

OR

BE BANNED FROM EATING IT EVER AGAIN?

IT'S A FACT!
Milk chocolate was invented by Daniel Peter, who sold the idea to his neighbour, Henri Nestlé.

IT'S A FACT!
Rubbing the groove between your lips and your nose in a circular fashion is said to help get rid of cravings for sweets and chocolates.

IT'S A FACT!
Chocolate manufacturers currently use 40 per cent of the world's almonds and 20 per cent of the world's peanuts.

LIVE ONE HUNDRED YEARS AS A VEGETARIAN
OR
FIFTY YEARS EATING ONLY BURGERS AND SAUSAGES?

IT'S A FACT! Sausages are even older than the ancient Greeks or Romans – it is known that they were being made around five thousand years ago.

IT'S A FACT! Sausages were first nicknamed 'bangers' during the Second World War. Because of rationing, they contained less meat and more water. As the sausages cooked, the water turned to steam – and the sausages would explode!

HAVE A TEN-MINUTE BOUT OF HICCUPS OR A FIVE-MINUTE SNEEZING FIT?

IT'S A FACT!
On average a bout of hiccups lasts five minutes.

IT'S A FACT!
Boys get hiccups more often than girls do.

IT'S A FACT!
When you sneeze, your heart stops.

IT'S A FACT!
You can't sneeze in your sleep.

HAVE TO USE A PUBLIC TOILET EVERY DAY FOR A MONTH

OR

GO BEHIND A BUSH IN THE SCHOOL YARD ONCE?

IT'S A FACT! The stall closest to the door in a public toilet is the cleanest, because it is the least used.

HAVE ONE HUGE EYE THAT TAKES UP HALF YOUR FACE OR EIGHT TINY EYES SCATTERED ACROSS YOUR BODY?

IT'S A FACT! In ancient Greece, a cyclops was a giant with one single eye in the middle of his head. The Greeks believed that a cyclops may have given the god Zeus his famous thunderbolt.

BE COVERED IN FUR OR COVERED IN SCALES?

IT'S A FACT! Butterfly wings are covered in thousands of tiny scales, which you can see by looking through a microscope.

SIT IN A BATH OF YOUR OWN SICK FOR FIVE MINUTES OR EAT YOUR OWN SICK TWICE?

IT'S A FACT! At royal feasts in Tudor England, guests would often make themselves sick in between courses so that they could carry on eating.

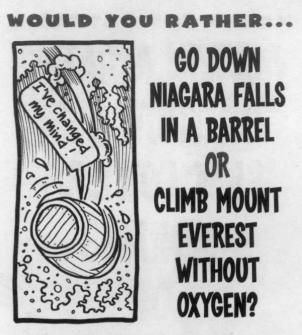

GO DOWN NIAGARA FALLS IN A BARREL OR CLIMB MOUNT EVEREST WITHOUT OXYGEN?

IT'S A FACT! Niagara Falls has moved about ten miles upstream in the last ten thousand years.

IT'S A FACT! In 1911, Bobby Leach, a British-born circus star, became the first man to go over Niagara Falls in a barrel and survive (although he ended up in hospital for twenty-three weeks). Fifteen years later, he died . . . after slipping on a piece of orange peel.

WOULD YOU RATHER...

CRY TEARS OF WEE OR SPIT POO?

JUST FOR FUN! Why did the biscuit cry? Because his mum and dad had been a wafer so long.

IT'S A FACT! Humans are the only animals that cry.

HAVE ONE SCOOP OF CHOCOLATE FUDGE BROWNIE ICE CREAM WITH WHIPPED CREAM AND A CHOCOLATE FLAKE

OR

FIVE SCOOPS OF PLAIN VANILLA?

IT'S A FACT! Ice-cream cones were first served at the 1904 World's Fair in St Louis, America.

WOULD YOU RATHER...

HAVE TWENTY GOOD FRIENDS OR ONE TRUE SOULMATE?

WISE WORDS! 'Friendship is born at that moment when one person says to another, "What! You too? I thought I was the only one."' (C. S. Lewis)

LOOK LIKE SHREK OR SMELL LIKE ROTTEN EGGS?

IT'S A FACT! There's a place in Austria called Rottenegg.

BE THREE FEET TALL OR EIGHT FEET TALL?

IT'S A FACT!

Robert Wadlow was the tallest man who ever lived. He was close to nine feet tall when he died.

WOULD YOU RATHER...

WIN £100,000 IN ONE GO OR £5,000 A YEAR FOR THE REST OF YOUR LIFE?

WISE WORDS! 'Wealth is the slave of a wise man, the master of a fool.' (Seneca)

GO WITHOUT TALKING FOR THREE DAYS

OR

HAVE TO SPEAK TOTAL NONSENSE FOR A WEEK?

IT'S A FACT! 'Jabberwocky' was the title of a nonsense poem written by *Alice in Wonderland* author Lewis Carroll. Most of the words in it were completely made up, but some of them – like 'chortle' – are still used today.

BE SIMON COWELL OR JUSTIN BIEBER?

IT'S A FACT! Simon Cowell is allergic to lamb's wool.

IT'S A FACT! Justin Bieber was once sent a rubber golf club by a fan. Very strange!

NEVER BE ABLE TO DIE

OR

DIE IN A YEAR'S TIME?

WISE WORDS! 'To the well-organized mind, death is but the next great adventure.' (J. K. Rowling)

WOULD YOU RATHER...

BE REINCARNATED AS A STUPID HUMAN OR AS A TALENTED DOG?

IT'S A FACT! The actor William H. Macy once said that he was a dog – a golden retriever – in a previous life.

BE TRAPPED FOR ONE HOUR IN A LIFT

OR

LOCKED IN YOUR BEDROOM FOR A DAY?

IT'S A FACT! In 2007, a man named Nicholas White was trapped in a lift – for forty-one hours. He had been working late one Friday night, and was about to go home when the lift jammed between floors. He had no water, food, watch or mobile phone. He was finally rescued on Monday morning – and was able to watch his ordeal all over again on the lift's CCTV.

LIVE IN THE BUSIEST PLACE IN THE WHOLE WORLD OR OUT IN THE WILDERNESS?

IT'S A FACT! If you gave each human on earth an equal portion of land, everyone would get roughly thirty square metres.

WRITE A TWO-HUNDRED-WORD ESSAY WITHOUT THE LETTER 'E'
OR
A FOUR-HUNDRED-WORD ESSAY WITHOUT THE LETTER 'A'?

IT'S A FACT! In Paris in 1816, J. R. Ronden tried to stage a play that didn't contain the letter 'A'. The audience was offended, rioted and refused to allow the play to finish.

BE AN ONLY CHILD OR HAVE SEVEN BROTHERS AND SISTERS?

IT'S A FACT! In 2009, a set of octuplets were born in California: six brothers and two sisters. They're the first full set of octuplets ever to have survived.

WOULD YOU RATHER...

LICK YOUR OWN TOILET SEAT
OR
YOUR TEACHER'S TOOTHBRUSH?

IT'S A FACT! Dentists recommend that a toothbrush be kept at least two metres away from a toilet to avoid airborne particles resulting from the flush.

EAT ONE JAR OF PEANUT BUTTER

OR

THREE JARS OF STRAWBERRY JAM IN ONE SITTING?

IT'S A FACT! Peanut butter was first introduced at the 1904 World's Fair in St Louis, America – the same place ice-cream cones were first seen!

RUN A MARATHON

OR

SWIM THE ENGLISH CHANNEL?

IT'S A FACT! Gordon Ramsay, Katie Holmes and Will Ferrell have all run marathons, while David Walliams swam the English Channel.

WOULD YOU RATHER...

VISIT THE SARDINE MUSEUM (IN FRANCE)
OR
THE BANANA MUSEUM (IN MARTINIQUE)?

JUST FOR FUN! Other unusual museums include the Mustard Museum (in America), the Matchbox Museum (in Portugal), or . . . the Centre for Unusual Museums (in Germany).

WOULD YOU RATHER...

WITH NO ANAESTHETIC AT ALL, HAVE YOUR APPENDIX OUT OR YOUR TONSILS REMOVED?

JUST FOR FUN! Two tonsils are sitting side by side, and one's wearing a smart bow tie. The other tonsil comments, 'You look very dressed up! What's the occasion?' His friend replies excitedly, 'Didn't you hear? The doctor's taking us out tonight!'

GO EVERYWHERE WALKING BACKWARDS OR CRAWLING ON YOUR HANDS AND KNEES?

IT'S A FACT! Penguins cannot walk backwards. They are too heavy on top, and their feet are too small for them to balance their weight.

WOULD YOU RATHER...

HAVE A BUCKET STUCK ON YOUR FOOT FOR A DAY

OR

A GLASS BOTTLE STUCK ON YOUR NOSE FOR AN HOUR?

IT'S A FACT!
The foot is the part of the body most often bitten by insects.

IT'S A FACT!
The cartilage in the nose never stops growing, which is why you see old people with big noses.

HAVE TO SQUIRT TOMATO KETCHUP ON EVERY SINGLE MEAL, EVEN BREAKFAST

OR

MAYONNAISE?

IT'S A FACT! Ketchup was originally made from fish broth and mushrooms. Tomatoes were added later.

IT'S A FACT! Mayonnaise was invented in 1756, to celebrate the victory of the French over the English at the battle of Port Mahon.

BE BLIND FOR THREE WEEKS OR DEAF FOR A YEAR?

IT'S A FACT! Vision requires more brain power than the other four senses (hearing, taste, feeling and smell).

HAVE ONE REALLY MEAN BIG SISTER

OR

THREE REALLY SMELLY LITTLE BROTHERS?

IT'S A FACT! The US State of Oregon has one city named Sisters and another called Brothers. Sisters got its name from a nearby trio of peaks in the Cascade Mountains known as the Three Sisters. Brothers was named as a counterpart to Sisters.

MEET FATHER CHRISTMAS BUT BE SWORN TO SECRECY

OR

SEE THE LOCH NESS MONSTER BUT HAVE NO PROOF?

IT'S A FACT!

4 per cent of people in Britain actually believe in the Loch Ness Monster.

JUST FOR FUN!

Why does Santa Claus have a garden? He likes to hoe hoe hoe.

ONLY EAT SQUARE FOOD FOR THE REST OF YOUR LIFE

OR

TRIANGULAR FOOD?

IT'S A FACT! 72 per cent of people in Britain prefer triangular sandwiches. They seem to taste better because they encourage a small bite, releasing flavour molecules more effectively.

WOULD YOU RATHER...

HAVE TO MAKE SIX VISITS TO THE TOILET (TO POO) IN ONE DAY
OR
NOT BE ALLOWED TO GO FOR SIX DAYS?

IT'S A FACT! The average person will spend six months of their life on the toilet.

WOULD YOU RATHER...

WALK ON BURNING COALS

OR

WALK ON COLD CUSTARD?

IT'S A FACT! You could actually walk on custard because it will get thick when pressure is applied to it.

WOULD YOU RATHER...

TURN EVERYTHING YOU TOUCHED TO SOLID GOLD

OR

TO DELICIOUS CHOCOLATE TRUFFLES?

IT'S A FACT! King Midas was granted the power to turn everything he touched to gold by the god Dionysus. But as soon as he felt hungry and wanted to eat something, he realized he had a problem!

HAVE A BEST FRIEND WHO DOESN'T USE TOOTHPASTE OR ONE WHO DOESN'T USE SHAMPOO?

IT'S A FACT! The Romans used powdered mouse brains as toothpaste.

WOULD YOU RATHER...

BE ABLE TO TALK IN DOG LANGUAGE
OR
HAVE A DOG THAT COULD SPEAK ENGLISH TO YOU (BUT ONLY WHEN NO ONE ELSE WAS AROUND)?

IT'S A FACT! Dogs can use almost every part of their body to communicate. For example, ears pricked forwards means a dog is paying close attention, while a tail between the legs means a dog is frightened.

WOULD YOU RATHER...

HAVE THE BRAINS OF A DOLPHIN IN THE BODY OF AN ANT
OR
THE BRAINS OF A SLUG IN THE BODY OF A POWERFUL LION?

IT'S A FACT! Dolphins are extremely intelligent and use something called echolocation to locate food, family and any dangerous predators, by sending out clicks that are bounced back to them by objects in the water.

WOULD YOU RATHER...

GO COMPLETELY
BALD AND HAVE TO WEAR A WIG
MADE FROM RAT FUR
OR
LOSE ALL YOUR TEETH AND
HAVE TO WEAR DENTURES
THAT ONCE BELONGED TO A
NINETY-YEAR-OLD LADY?

FIGHT A DUEL WITH RUBBER SWORDS OR WATER PISTOLS?

IT'S A FACT! The French writer Sainte-Beuve was involved in a duel with the owner of *Le Globe* newspaper. When asked to choose his weapons, he replied, 'I choose spelling. You're dead.'

HAVE A NEW PLANET NAMED AFTER YOU

OR

NAME A NASTY NEW TYPE OF BEETLE AFTER YOUR WORST ENEMY?

IT'S A FACT! Earth is the only planet not named after a god.

IT'S A FACT! 19367 Pink Floyd is an asteroid between Mars and Jupiter and was named in honour of the famous rock band.

WALK TO SCHOOL EVERY DAY IN THE POURING RAIN
OR
BE DRIVEN THERE, BUT ALWAYS GET CAR SICK AS YOU PULL UP AT THE SCHOOL GATES?

WISE WORDS! 'I hated school. Even to this day, when I see a school bus it's just depressing to me. The poor little kids.' (Dolly Parton)

HAVE DIMPLES IN YOUR CHEEKS OR FRECKLES EVERYWHERE?

IT'S A FACT! The attachment of the human skin to muscles is what causes dimples.

HAVE HOMER SIMPSON (SLOW BUT NICE) AS YOUR FATHER
OR
MR BURNS (NASTY BUT RICH)?

IT'S A FACT! Dan Castellaneta based the voice of Homer on his own father's voice.

IT'S A FACT! The door knocker on the Simpsons' front door looks a lot like Mr Burns – complete with liver spots and pointy nose.

WOULD YOU RATHER...

BE ABLE TO WIGGLE YOUR EARS IN TIME TO MUSIC
OR
BE ABLE TO FART THE TUNE OF 'HAPPY BIRTHDAY'?

IT'S A FACT! An eleven-year-old American boy farted 217 times in five minutes on a radio call-in show.

BE MICKEY MOUSE FOR A WEEK OR DONALD DUCK?

IT'S A FACT! Quackmore Duck is the name of Donald Duck's father. Donald also has a sister called Dumbella.

SWIM THREE LENGTHS IN A POOL THAT SOMEONE HAS JUST PEED IN

OR

ONE LENGTH IN A POOL THAT SOMEONE HAS JUST BEEN SICK IN?

IT'S A FACT! SWIMS is the longest word with 180-degree rotational symmetry – which means that it reads the same way upside down.

SIT DOWN IN THE TOILET AND FIND JUST ONE SHEET OF SOFT TOILET PAPER LEFT

OR

YOUR FAVOURITE BOOK THAT YOU HAVE TO RIP UP AND USE?

IT'S A FACT! Before the invention of toilet paper, people used shells or stones, bunches of herbs, or a bit of sponge attached to a stick which they rinsed with cold water.

EAT A RAW CHILLI OR A RAW ONION?

IT'S A FACT!

An onion, apple and potato all have the same taste. The differences in flavour are caused by their smell.

IT'S A FACT!

Chillies have been eaten since at least 7000 BC in South America, and at one point were used as currency.

BE HARRY POTTER OR EDWARD CULLEN?

IT'S A FACT!

Robert Pattinson – who plays Edward Cullen in the *Twilight* movies – learned to drive in a ten hour crash course on the set of *Twilight*.

IT'S A FACT!

Daniel Radcliffe – who plays Harry Potter – can rotate his arm 360 degrees.

WOULD YOU RATHER...

WAKE UP UNDERNEATH A PILE OF DEAD SQUIRRELS
OR
GO TO SLEEP WITH A LIVE FROG IN YOUR BED?

JUST FOR FUN! I slept like a log last night . . . I woke up in the fireplace.

WOULD YOU RATHER...

BE ABLE TO MAKE THE PRIME MINISTER SAY, 'BOGEYBALLS' IN THE HOUSE OF COMMONS
OR
BE AN OLYMPIC ATHLETE FOR A DAY?

IT'S A FACT! Margaret Thatcher was the UK's first female Prime Minister, and also the first in Europe.

BE IN AN ARMY OF SHEEP LED BY A LION

OR

IN AN ARMY OF LIONS LED BY A SHEEP?

IT'S A FACT! Australia, Uruguay, Syria and Bolivia all have more sheep than people. Baaaa!

LISTEN TO FINGERNAILS SCRAPING DOWN A BLACKBOARD FOR TEN MINUTES

OR

LISTEN TO A TINY BABY CRYING FOR FIVE MINUTES?

IT'S A FACT! Fingernails grow four times faster than toenails.

TASTE CHOCOLATE EVERY TIME YOU ATE SOMETHING, BUT SMELL ROTTEN EGGS OR VICE VERSA?

IT'S A FACT! Humans can distinguish between three thousand and ten thousand different smells.

WOULD YOU RATHER...

DRINK A PINT OF SOUR COW'S MILK
OR
A GLASS OF FRESH PIG'S MILK?

IT'S A FACT! A cow gives nearly two hundred thousand glasses of milk in her lifetime.

IT'S A FACT! Pigs are the cleanest farm animals. They will even take a shower if one is available.

HAVE THREE ARMS OR THIRTY FINGERS?

JUST FOR FUN!

A man went to the doctor and said, 'I've hurt my arm in several places.' The doctor replied, 'Well, I recommend you don't visit any of them again.'

LIVE IN A HOUSE BUILT FROM HOT MACARONI CHEESE

OR

HAVE TO WEAR A HAT TO SCHOOL MADE FROM COLD LEFTOVER LASAGNE?

IT'S A FACT! 'Vermicelli' – a popular type of pasta – literally means 'little worms'.

WOULD YOU RATHER...

EAT A DEAD SPIDER
OR
A LIVE FLY?

IT'S A FACT! When a female spider dies, she is eaten by her babies.

SLEEP IN THE SAME ROOM AS FOUR MICE

OR

TWO RATS?

IT'S A FACT! Rats are omnivorous, which means they eat almost any kind of food, including dead and dying members of their own species.

WOULD YOU RATHER...
BECOME A FAMOUS SINGER
OR
A BRAIN SURGEON?

IT'S A FACT! Scientists have performed brain surgery on cockroaches.

HAVE A QUAVER WHERE YOUR ARM SHOULD BE

OR

A TWIGLET WHERE YOUR NOSE SHOULD BE?

IT'S A FACT! A quaver is a type of musical note, also known as an eighth note.

CLEAN THE BATH WITH YOUR TONGUE
OR
SCOOP UP A COWPAT WITH YOUR BARE HANDS?

JUST FOR FUN! What do little calves get when they do well at Cow School? A pat on the head.

MOVE TO A COMPLETELY NEW COUNTRY EVERY MONTH FOR THE REST OF YOUR LIFE

OR

STAY IN YOUR HOME FOR EVER, WITHOUT LEAVING FOR EVEN A MINUTE?

IT'S A FACT! People who are afraid of leaving their homes are called agoraphobes. Charles Darwin is thought to have been a famous agoraphobe.

STEAL A BONE FROM A ROTTWEILER

OR

KILL A KITTEN?

IT'S A FACT! If a dog has a diet rich in bones then its poo will be white.

BE SIX FEET TALL IN A WORLD WHERE EVERYONE ELSE IS TWELVE FEET TALL
OR
FOUR FEET TALL IN A WORLD WHERE EVERYONE ELSE IS TWO FEET TALL?

IT'S A FACT!

An Austrian man named Adam Rainer is the only man in recorded human history ever to have been both a dwarf and a giant. At the age of twenty-one he was less than four feet tall, but then he had growth spurts that saw him grow to an incredible seven feet eight inches.

WAKE UP UNEXPECTEDLY IN HOSPITAL MISSING THREE FINGERS OR IN THE STREET WITH A BLACK EYE BUT NO MEMORY OF WHAT HAPPENED?

IT'S A FACT! Male patients fall out of hospital beds twice as often as female patients.

YOUR BEST FRIEND WAS A REALLY SUCCESSFUL SINGER OR A HUGE FAILURE WHO MADE YOU LOOK MUCH BETTER?

JUST FOR FUN! If you and your friend are being chased by a mad dog, don't worry about outrunning the mad dog – just worry about outrunning your friend.

LIVE IN A GIANT SANDCASTLE
OR
AN IGLOO?

IT'S A FACT! According to a study done by students at Bournemouth University, Torre Abbey Sands in Torquay is the best beach in the country for sandcastles. It has extremely fine-grained sand with exceptional cohesive (binding) powers. For the best sandcastles you need eight parts sand to one part water.

WEAR THE SAME PAIR OF PANTS EVERY DAY FOR A YEAR OR THE SAME SOCKS?

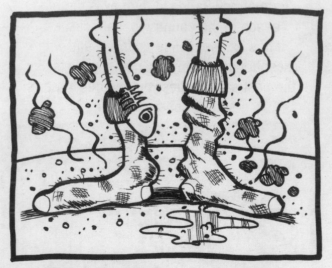

IT'S A FACT! When Albert Einstein was inducted as an American citizen, he attended the ceremony without socks.

COME FACE TO FACE WITH A TIGER (WHILE WEARING SCUBA-DIVING EQUIPMENT) IN THE SEA OR A SHARK (WHILE ON A SKATEBOARD) ON LAND?

IT'S A FACT! Tigers have striped skin, not just striped fur.

IT'S A FACT! One species of shark is so competitive that the babies fight each other within the womb, until only one is left to be born alive.

SWIM A LENGTH OF YOUR LOCAL SWIMMING POOL WITH A TEN-KILOGRAM WEIGHT TIED TO YOUR TUMMY

OR

A ONE-KILOGRAM WEIGHT TIED TO EACH HAND?

IT'S A FACT! There are more than a million swimming pools in Florida, even though the sea is never more than eighty miles away.

ALWAYS HAVE TO SPEAK BACKWARDS

OR

ALWAYS HAVE TO SPEAK IN VERSE?

JUST FOR FUN! A palindrome is a word or sentence that reads the same backwards or forwards – for example, 'A nut for a jar of tuna'.

BE ABLE TO PREDICT THE FUTURE OR BE ABLE TO CHANGE THREE MAJOR EVENTS IN HISTORY?

WISE WORDS! 'There is always one moment in childhood when the door opens and lets the future in.' (Graham Greene)

DIVE FROM TWENTY METRES INTO THE SEA

OR

BELLY-FLOP FROM TEN METRES?

IT'S A FACT! The sound you hear when you put a shell to your ear is not the sea, but blood flowing through your head.

ALWAYS WRITE WITH YOUR 'WRONG' HAND
OR
ALWAYS WRITE WITH YOUR 'RIGHT' HAND, BUT WITH A PEN THAT IS ALWAYS RUNNING OUT OF INK?

IT'S A FACT! Offered a new pen to try, 97 per cent of people will write their own name.

WOULD YOU RATHER...

EAT A (COOKED) COW'S BRAIN OR A (COOKED) CAT'S LEG?

Moo!

JUST FOR FUN! Some rather unusual dishes from around the world include pig's organs in blood sauce (from the Philippines), roast field mice (Mexico) and red ant chutney (India). Hungry, anyone?

WOULD YOU RATHER...

PEOPLE COULD READ YOUR MIND
OR
COULD SEE YOU
NAKED AT ANY TIME?

IT'S A FACT! Mind-reading is also known as telepathy, a gift that many identical twins claim to have. In the Harry Potter books, it's called legilimency.

SMELL OF NEWLY-OPENED CRAYONS OR SMELL OF COOKED CABBAGE?

IT'S A FACT! When you open a new box of crayons, the scent you can smell is that of stearic acid, which is beef fat.

HAVE EYEBALLS THE SIZE OF PING-PONG BALLS
OR
EARS THE SIZE OF AN ELEPHANT'S?

IT'S A FACT! Some people have the rare ability to pop out their eyeballs – one American woman did just that on live TV. Imagine how scary that would be for people suffering from ommetaphobia – the fear of eyes!

RUN ONE MILE IN SIX-INCH HEELS

OR

SWIM HALF A MILE IN HANDCUFFS?

IT'S A FACT! Before the sixteenth century, shoes didn't have heels. Queen Elizabeth I had them added to give the Royal Family additional stature.

HAVE TO LIVE WITH YOUR GRANDPARENTS

OR

NOT HAVE ANY GRANDPARENTS?

JUST FOR FUN! When a class of eight-year-olds were asked to explain what grandparents were, one little boy said, 'Usually grandmothers are fat – but not too fat to tie your shoes.'

BE ADOPTED BY A FAMOUS BUT MEAN FILM STAR

OR

LIVE WITH YOUR OWN LOVING FAMILY IN POVERTY?

IT'S A FACT! Some famous people who were adopted as children include Marilyn Monroe, Roman Abramovich, Andy McNab and Nelson Mandela.

BE A SHORT BUT FAST BASKETBALL PLAYER
OR
A FAT BUT GRACEFUL BALLERINA?

IT'S A FACT! Basketball players are very superstitious about bouncing the ball before taking a foul shot. They also wipe the soles of their sneakers for good luck.

INHABIT YOUR BROTHER OR SISTER'S BODY FOR THREE HOURS OR YOUR LEAST FAVOURITE TEACHER'S?

IT'S A FACT! *The Body Snatchers* is a sci-fi novel from 1955 about alien seeds that drift down to earth and replace sleeping human people with perfect alien replicas, while the originals turn to dust. Creepy!

ALWAYS HAVE TO WASH IN ICE-COLD WATER

OR

NOT WASH AT ALL FOR THREE WEEKS?

IT'S A FACT! Just 55 per cent of men wash their hands after using the toilet, while 80 per cent of women do.

BECOME ALLERGIC TO YOUR FAVOURITE FOOD OR TO THE FAMILY PET?

IT'S A FACT! More people are allergic to cow's milk than to any other food.

PUBLISH YOUR DIARY
OR
HAVE YOUR BEST FRIEND REVEAL YOUR BIGGEST SECRET?

WISE WORDS! 'If you reveal your secrets to the wind you should not blame the wind for revealing them to the trees.' (Kahlil Gibran)

SELL YOUR BELOVED PET FOR £50 OR YOUR LITTLE SISTER FOR £150?

JUST FOR FUN! People give their pets the weirdest names. Wayne Rooney has a chow-chow called Fizz, while Reese Witherspoon has a bulldog named Frank Sinatra.

LICK A SMELLY TOILET SEAT
OR
LET OFF A STINK BOMB IN A TOILET AT SCHOOL AND HAVE TO TELL EVERYONE IT WAS YOUR FART?

IT'S A FACT! In 1986, Nathan Hicks of St Louis, Missouri shot his brother Herbert dead because he had used six toilet rolls in two days.

ALWAYS LOSE AT FOOTBALL MATCHES

OR

BE GOOD AT FOOTBALL, BUT NEVER BE INVITED TO PLAY?

IT'S A FACT! In 1980, the Liberian football team playing against Gambia were threatened with the firing squad if they lost. Luckily for them, they drew.

BE CHASED BY THE POLICE
OR
A GANG OF ANGRY CRIMINALS?

JUST FOR FUN! The police arrested two kids yesterday. One was drinking battery acid, the other was eating fireworks. They charged one – and let the other one off.

HAVE ALL YOUR MAJOR LIFE DECISIONS BE MADE BY THE TOSS OF A COIN

OR

BY A TOTAL STRANGER?

IT'S A FACT! The city of Portland in the state of Oregon was named in a coin toss in 1844. Heads was Portland, tails was Boston.

WEAR A T-SHIRT WITH A PICTURE OF YOUR MUM ON IT EVERY DAY

OR

STAND UP IN ASSEMBLY AND SHOUT, 'I HAVE THE BEST TEACHER IN THE WORLD!'?

WISE WORDS! 'Parents were invented to make children happy by giving them something to ignore.' (Ogden Nash)

LOSE YOUR SIGHT, BUT HAVE AMAZING UNDERWATER HEARING
OR
LOSE YOUR HEARING, BUT BE ABLE TO SEE IN THE DARK?

IT'S A FACT! Our hearing is less sharp after eating too much.

IT'S A FACT! A dolphin's hearing is so acute that it can pick up an underwater sound from fifteen miles away.

BE ABDUCTED BY ALIENS BUT TREATED LIKE ROYALTY ON YOUR NEW PLANET

OR

MANAGE TO ESCAPE, BUT NEVER BE ABLE TO TELL YOUR FRIENDS WHAT HAPPENED TO YOU?

IT'S A FACT! Over a quarter of people who are kidnapped and taken hostage grow to like their captors. This is called 'Stockholm syndrome' after a group of Swedish bank workers were kidnapped by robbers, and defended them once they had been freed!

WOULD YOU RATHER...

LOSE YOUR HAIR PERMANENTLY
OR
HAVE A HUGE WART ON YOUR NOSE FOR LIFE?

IT'S A FACT! A human being loses around forty to one hundred strands of hair a day.

WOULD YOU RATHER...

LIVE IN A LIGHTHOUSE HAUNTED BY THE GHOSTS OF SAILORS

OR

A WINDMILL SURROUNDED BY SPOOKY SCARECROWS?

IT'S A FACT! Windmills turn anti-clockwise.

EAT A RAW EGG (INCLUDING THE SHELL) OR A CHICKEN'S BEAK?

IT'S A FACT! An ostrich egg weighs the same as twenty-four chicken eggs.

HAVE THE POWER TO BE INVISIBLE OR THE POWER TO FLY?

WISE WORDS! 'The true mystery of the world is the visible – not the invisible.' (Oscar Wilde)

WOULD YOU RATHER...
FIND A SPIDER UP YOUR SLEEVE
OR
A WORM IN YOUR LUNCHBOX?

IT'S A FACT!
Spiders can't eat solid food so they have to liquefy their prey before consuming it.

IT'S A FACT!
Some ribbon worms will eat bits of themselves if they can't find any food.

TRAVEL BACK IN TIME JUST ONCE OR WRITE THREE WEEKS OF THE FUTURE?

WISE WORDS! 'History will be kind to me, for I intend to write it.' (Sir Winston Churchill)

WOULD YOU RATHER...

LIVE IN AN UNDERGROUND CAVE OR UP A TREE?

IT'S A FACT! There are over four thousand caves in Bulgaria.

HAVE THE LOUDEST MOBILE PHONE RINGTONE IN THE WHOLE SCHOOL

OR

ONE FEATURING YOUR MOTHER SAYING, 'PICK UP THE PHONE, SNOOKUMS!'?

IT'S A FACT! There are now more mobile phones than people in Britain.

HAVE TO SLEEP WITH A BLACK WIDOW SPIDER DOWN YOUR PANTS FOR A WEEK OR FALL ASLEEP FOR A WHOLE YEAR?

IT'S A FACT! The black widow can devour as many as twenty 'mates' in a single day.

STOP TIME OR ACCELERATE TIME?

WISE WORDS! 'Time flies like an arrow. Fruit flies like a banana.' (Groucho Marx)

WOULD YOU RATHER...

SIT IN A BATH FULL OF BAKED BEANS FOR FIVE MINUTES

OR

STAND UNDER AN ICE-COLD SHOWER FOR TEN MINUTES?

IT'S A FACT! The British eat more cans of baked beans than the rest of the world combined.

BEAT UP THE SCHOOL BULLY

OR

BECOME HIS OR HER NEW BEST FRIEND?

IT'S A FACT! Celebrities who were bullied at school include Tom Cruise and Victoria Beckham.

WOULD YOU RATHER...
BE A SHARK
OR
A DOLPHIN?

IT'S A FACT! Sharks are immune to all known diseases.

IT'S A FACT! Dolphins jump out of the water to conserve energy as it's easier to move through the air than through the water.

HAVE TO WEAR A BICYCLE HELMET FOR THE REST OF YOUR LIFE OR A 'KICK ME' SIGN?

IT'S A FACT! There are twice as many bicycles in the world as cars.

BE IGNORED BY EVERYONE FOR A WHOLE DAY
OR
HAVE TO GIVE A TEN-MINUTE SPEECH TO THE WHOLE SCHOOL?

WISE WORDS! 'A child educated only at school is an uneducated child.' (George Santayana)

BE ALLERGIC TO SUGAR
OR
ADDICTED TO SUGAR?

IT'S A FACT!
There are sweeteners that are about two hundred thousand times sweeter than sugar.

IT'S A FACT!
Writer George Bernard Shaw was asked if he knew that 'sugar' was the only word in the English language where 'su' was pronounced 'sh'. He replied, 'Sure.'

BE IN AN EARTHQUAKE

OR

IN A HURRICANE?

IT'S A FACT! In ten minutes, a hurricane releases more energy than all the world's nuclear weapons combined.

IT'S A FACT! Two minor earthquakes occur every minute.

SPEND A YEAR LIVING IN A TENT

OR

ON A TINY FISHING BOAT?

IT'S A FACT! The ancient Egyptians built the first sailing boats.

WOULD YOU RATHER...

RIDE A GALLOPING ANGRY BULL
OR
SKI DOWN A MOUNTAIN
BACKWARDS?

IT'S A FACT! Bull riding has been called 'the most dangerous eight seconds in sports'.

BE BRUCE WAYNE (BATMAN'S ALTER EGO) WITHOUT ANY SUPERPOWERS

OR

CLARK KENT (SUPERMAN'S ALTER EGO)?

IT'S A FACT! Clark Kent, the name of Superman's alter ego, was derived from the names of the Hollywood stars Clark Gable and Kent Taylor.

HAVE A MISSING TOE OR AN EXTRA FINGER?

IT'S A FACT! The most sensitive finger is the forefinger.

BE CAUGHT SINGING LADY GAGA SONGS IN THE SHOWER
OR
BE CAUGHT HAVING AN ARGUMENT WITH YOURSELF (AND LOSING)?

IT'S A FACT! Lady Gaga's real name is Stefani Germanotta and one of her school nicknames was 'the Germ'.

WOULD YOU RATHER...

HAVE A MOUTHFUL OF ANTS
OR
A BUM FULL OF CATERPILLARS?

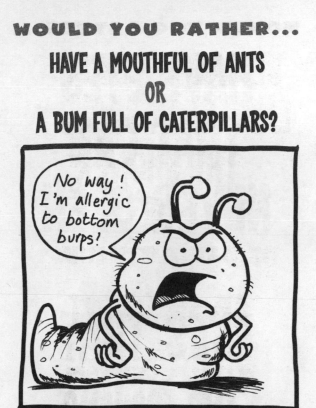

IT'S A FACT!
Humans, ants and chimpanzees are the only beings that wage war.

IT'S A FACT!
The average caterpillar has two thousand muscles in its body (humans have under seven hundred).

HAVE EYES THAT CAN NEVER OPEN

OR

EYES THAT CAN NEVER SHUT?

IT'S A FACT! Our eyes are made up of more than two million working parts.

BE THE FATTEST KING OR QUEEN IN HISTORY
OR
THE WORLD'S MOST GORGEOUS SERVANT?

IT'S A FACT! King Louis the Fat
(King Louis VI of France) ruled France
from 1108 to 1137.

GO TO SLEEP WITH A RAW ONION ON YOUR PILLOW
OR
RAW GARLIC?

IT'S A FACT! Cut an onion in half, rub it on the sole of your foot and an hour later you'll taste onion in your mouth.

EAT A SPOONFUL OF MOUSE MEAT

OR

ONE LIVE WORM?

IT'S A FACT! In ancient China, mouse meat was considered a delicacy.

WAKE UP AS A FLESH-EATING ZOMBIE OR A BLOODSUCKING VAMPIRE?

IT'S A FACT! In some South African cultures, it's believed that a small child has the power to turn a dead body into a zombie. So watch out for your little brother or sister . . .

GO WITHOUT PEAS FOR THE REST OF YOUR LIFE OR CARROTS?

IT'S A FACT! The oldest known vegetable is the pea.

IT'S A FACT! Children celebrating their birthday in Brazil get sweets shaped like fruit and vegetables. Because these sweets are so beautifully made, the children try to leave them for a while before they eat them.

WOULD YOU RATHER...

LEARN TO EAT FIRE
OR
TO SWALLOW SWORDS?

IT'S A FACT! The bark of the redwood tree is fireproof. Fires in redwood forests take place inside the trees.

MEET ROALD DAHL
OR
J. K. ROWLING?

IT'S A FACT! Roald Dahl based the character of the grandmother in *The Witches* on his own mother.

EAT FIFTY PIECES OF BUTTERSCOTCH OR TEN PACKETS OF CUSTARD CREAM BISCUITS?

IT'S A FACT! There is real butter in butterscotch (but no Scotch).

FIND A TWINKLING DIAMOND RING IN THE STREET

OR

A TINY STRAY PUPPY?

IT'S A FACT! The only thing that can destroy a diamond is intense heat.

SWIM WITH JELLYFISH FOR TEN MINUTES
OR
SIT ON AN ANTHILL FOR THREE MINUTES?

IT'S A FACT! Jellyfish are 95 per cent water, and sometimes evaporate if stranded on a beach.

GO TO SCHOOL ON CHRISTMAS DAY OR FOR A WEEK IN THE SUMMER HOLIDAYS?

IT'S A FACT! In the US state of Indiana, there is a town called Santa Claus.

HAVE A FURRY GREEN COATING ON YOUR TEETH THAN CAN NEVER BE CLEANED OFF
OR
THREE SWOLLEN PURPLE BOILS ON YOUR FOREHEAD FOR A WHOLE YEAR?

IT'S A FACT! In 1974, Philip Grundy, a dentist, left his dental nurse £181,000 in his will on the condition that she didn't wear any make-up or jewellery or go out with anyone for five years.

IT'S A FACT! Sugar was added to chewing gum in 1869 – by a dentist.

HAVE THE WORLD'S WORST SUNBURN OR THE WORLD'S WORST FROSTBITE?

IT'S A FACT! Besides humans, the only animal that can suffer sunburn is the pig.

IT'S A FACT! The great French sculptor Rodin died of frostbite in 1917 when the government refused him financial aid for a flat – yet they kept his statues safe and warm in museums.

PLAY TWISTER WITH A CONTORTIONIST

OR

HAVE A STARING CONTEST WITH AN OWL?

IT'S A FACT! An owl can see a mouse fifty metres away in light no brighter than a candle flame.

WOULD YOU RATHER...
ONLY EVER BE ABLE TO TWEET
OR
TEXT?

IT'S A FACT! The very first tweeter was Jack Dorsey, the man who created Twitter in 2006.

HAVE A FIGHT WITH A BLINDFOLDED VELOCIRAPTOR
OR
A GOLIATH SPIDER?

IT'S A FACT! The goliath spider has teeth as big as a cheetah's claws. Yes, that is HUGE.

IT'S A FACT! A game popular with young people in Afghanistan is 'kite fighting.' The kite strings are covered with a mixture of flour and powdered glass and participants try to cut through the strings of their opponents' kites.

HAVE TO STAND UP FOR A WHOLE YEAR

OR

HAVE TO SIT BARE-BUM ON A SEAT COVERED IN STINGING NETTLES?

IT'S A FACT!
Blackbird, chief of the Omaha Indians, was buried sitting on his favourite horse.

IT'S A FACT!
Besides humans, the only animal that can stand on its head is the elephant.

GIVE UP CHIPS FOR EVER OR FISH?

IT'S A FACT! These are the names of some genuine fish and chip shops: 'Don't Tell a Sole', 'The Starchip Enterprise', 'Codswallop', and 'The Frying Squad'.

EAT ROTTEN EGGS EVERY DAY FOR THE REST OF YOUR LIFE

OR

SCABBY CHICKEN SKIN?

JUST FOR FUN! Why didn't the chicken skeleton cross the road? Because he didn't have enough guts.

FORGET WHO YOU ARE FOR A YEAR
OR
GO TO JAIL FOR TWO YEARS?

IT'S A FACT! The first prisoner in the Tower of London, Ranulf Flambard, Bishop of Durham, was also the first person to escape from it. He used a rope smuggled to him by friends in a cask of wine.

HAVE A BATH IN MELTED CHEESE

OR

A SHOWER IN MUSHROOM SOUP?

JUST FOR FUN! What cheese can you hide a horse in? Mascarpone.

HAVE A POCKET-SIZED BEST FRIEND
OR
A GIANT BEST FRIEND?

WISE WORDS! 'Your friends will know you better in the first minute you meet than your acquaintances will know you in a thousand years.' (Richard Bach)

HAVE ELEPHANT EARS OR DUCK FEET?

IT'S A FACT! In China, duck feet are a very popular dish.

BE ABLE TO SEE THROUGH WALLS OR SEE INTO PEOPLE'S MINDS?

IT'S A FACT! The people of East Anglia used to mummify cats and place them in the walls of their homes to ward off evil spirits.

ALWAYS KNOW WHEN IT'S GOING TO RAIN

OR

BE ABLE TO TURN THE RAIN INTO CHOCOLATE MILKSHAKE?

JUST FOR FUN! What do you get if you cross a cow, a camel and a monkey? Lumpy banana milkshake!

SPEAK ANY FOREIGN LANGUAGE OR BE ABLE TO PLAY ANY INSTRUMENT?

IT'S A FACT! Malayalam, spoken in Kerala, southern India, is the only language with a palindromic name – which means it reads the same backwards.

HAVE A PHOTOGRAPHIC MEMORY

OR

BE UNFORGETTABLE (IN A GOOD WAY!)?

IT'S A FACT! Bill Clinton, Bill Gates and Wolfgang Mozart all have (or had) photographic memories.

HAVE DINNER WITH THE QUEEN OR WITH YOUR FAVOURITE FILM STAR?

IT'S A FACT! The Queen has hundreds of people working for her, including the Keeper of the Queen's Swans, the Mistress of the Robes, the Queen's Raven Master, the Lady of the Bedchamber and the Queen's Racing Pigeon Manager.

WOULD YOU RATHER...

SIT NEXT TO THE NOISIEST PERSON IN SCHOOL
OR
SOMEONE WHO PICKS THEIR NOSE AND EATS IT?

WISE WORDS! 'Noise is the most impertinent of all forms of interruption. It is not only an interruption, but is also a disruption of thought.'
(Arthur Schopenhauer)

LIVE IN THE NINETEENTH CENTURY OR THE TWENTY-SECOND CENTURY?

IT'S A FACT! In the nineteenth century, people – including children – could be hanged for the smallest crime. In 1819, Thomas Wildish was hanged for letter-stealing, while in 1833, an unnamed nine-year-old boy was hanged for stealing a pennyworth of paint from a shop.

WOULD YOU RATHER...

BE A GHOST HUNTER
OR
A VAMPIRE HUNTER?

IT'S A FACT! We reach the peak of our ability to 'see' ghosts at the age of seven.

CRASH YOUR PARENTS' CAR OR GET A SPEEDING TICKET FOR DRIVING AT ONE HUNDRED MILES PER HOUR?

IT'S A FACT! In September 2004, a Minnesota state trooper issued a speeding ticket to a motorcyclist who was doing an incredible 205 miles per hour.

WIN THE LOTTERY BUT NEVER BE ABLE TO SHARE ANY OF YOUR WINNINGS WITH ANOTHER PERSON

OR

WIN THE LOTTERY BUT NEVER BE ALLOWED TO BUY ANYTHING FOR YOURSELF – JUST FOR OTHERS?

JUST FOR FUN! 'Son, if you really want something in this life, you have to work for it. Now quiet! They're about to announce the lottery numbers.' (Homer Simpson)

NEVER GO TO SCHOOL AGAIN OR NEVER GO ON HOLIDAY?

JUST FOR FUN! This was a genuine note sent by a parent to a teacher: 'Please exkuse John for being absent on January 28th, 29th, 30th, 31st, 32nd and 33rd.'

WRITE THE WORLD'S MOST FAMOUS BOOK

OR

BE THE STAR OF THE WORLD'S MOST SUCCESSFUL FILM?

IT'S A FACT!
The people of Iceland read more books than any other country in the world.

WISE WORDS!
'Books are divided into two classes, the books of the hour and the books of all time.' (John Ruskin)

LOSE BOTH YOUR THUMBS OR YOUR BIG TOES?

IT'S A FACT! Purlicue is the word for the space between the extended thumb and index finger.

WOULD YOU RATHER...

BE IN A JAIL CELL WITH THREE VERY SMELLY PRISONERS
OR
IN SOLITARY CONFINEMENT FOR A MONTH?

IT'S A FACT! The town of Churchill in Manitoba, Canada has a twenty-cell prison for polar bears that cause trouble – usually for scavenging in the town's rubbish dumps.

WOULD YOU RATHER...

ALWAYS HAVE TO DANCE (RATHER THAN WALK) OR ALWAYS HAVE TO SPIT WHEN YOU TALK?

IT'S A FACT! There's a place in Australia called Spit Junction.

HAVE TO LIVE IN A HOUSE WITHOUT CENTRAL HEATING IN THE COLDEST WINTER OR WITHOUT INTERNET?

IT'S A FACT! In Hungary, hot springs are used for central heating in homes.

WAKE TO FIND AN EVIL-LOOKING GHOST TAPPING ON YOUR BEDROOM WINDOW

OR

A HUNGRY WEREWOLF ABOUT TO TEAR DOWN YOUR BEDROOM DOOR?

IT'S A FACT! In the famous film *Werewolf of London*, the actor Henry Hull didn't want to spend hours with a make-up artist every day – so the werewolf he plays still has some very human features!

WASH YOUR PARENTS' CAR EVERY WEEK FOR A YEAR
OR
WASH THEIR UNDERWEAR EVERY DAY FOR A WEEK (BY HAND)?

IT'S A FACT! Rowan Atkinson (who plays Mr Bean) loves washing cars so much that he chose 'a car to clean' as his Desert Island Discs luxury.

BE ALLOWED TO LIE IN UNTIL TEN O'CLOCK EVERY MORNING, BUT HAVE TO SLEEP WITH COCKROACHES IN YOUR BED

OR

HAVE THE WORLD'S COMFIEST BED, BUT HAVE TO GET UP AT FIVE O'CLOCK EVERY DAY?

IT'S A FACT! The cicada, a fly found in Africa, spends seventeen years of its life sleeping. In the two weeks it's awake, it mates . . . and then dies.

BE JAMES BOND OR JASON BOURNE?

IT'S A FACT! Half the world's population has seen at least one James Bond film.

EAT A BADGER BRAIN BURGER OR A PORCUPINE PIZZA?

JUST FOR FUN! What sound do porcupines make when they kiss? Ouch!

WOULD YOU RATHER...

EAT A TRAMP'S TOENAIL
OR
DRINK DIRTY PUDDLE WATER?

IT'S A FACT! There's a place in Dorset named Puddletown.

BE A CHAMPION ARM-WRESTLER OR A FAMOUS DRUMMER?

IT'S A FACT! Chef Jamie Oliver used to play drums in a band named Scarlet Division, while Madonna drummed for a band named the Breakfast Club.

HAVE HOMER SIMPSON AS A FATHER OR MARGE SIMPSON AS A MOTHER?

IT'S A FACT! Homer's grunt – D'oh! – has entered the English dictionary.

HAVE A PEDIGREE PUPPY WHO BITES
OR
A SCRUFFY BUT SWEET MONGREL FROM BATTERSEA DOGS AND CATS HOME?

IT'S A FACT! People who have rescued animals from Battersea Dogs and Cats Home include Dame Jacqueline Wilson and Sir Elton John.

WOULD YOU RATHER...
YOUR FARTS SMELLED LIKE PERFUME
OR
SOUNDED LIKE MUSIC?

IT'S A FACT! 10 per cent of Britain's perfume sales take place at Heathrow Airport.

WOULD YOU RATHER...

BE A LION
OR
A LION-TAMER?

IT'S A FACT! Lions sleep for up to twenty hours a day. Lazy!

GO ON A ROLLERCOASTER JUST AFTER A HUGE LUNCH

OR

SIT NEXT TO SOMEONE ON A ROLLERCOASTER WHO'S JUST EATEN A HUGE LUNCH?

IT'S A FACT! Theme park attendance goes up after a fatal accident. It seems that people want to take the same ride that killed someone. Very odd . . .

DIE BY FIRE WHEN YOU'RE REALLY COLD

OR

DIE BY DROWNING WHEN YOU'RE REALLY THIRSTY?

IT'S A FACT! Fires usually move faster uphill than downhill.

WOULD YOU RATHER...

HAVE TO CELEBRATE CHRISTMAS EVERY SINGLE DAY OF THE YEAR
OR
NEVER CELEBRATE CHRISTMAS AT ALL?

JUST FOR FUN! What is Santa's favourite pizza? One that's deep pan, crisp and even.

LIVE IN A CAVE MADE OF FREEZING COLD ICE OR IN A CAVE MADE OF RED HOT STONES?

IT'S A FACT! The deepest cave found on earth is the Krubera Cave, near the Black Sea. It's over two thousand metres deep.

WOULD YOU RATHER...

BURP EVERY TIME SOMEONE SAID THE WORD 'HOMEWORK'
OR
FART EVERY TIME SOMEONE SAID THE WORD 'WEEKEND'?

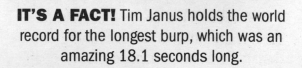

IT'S A FACT! Tim Janus holds the world record for the longest burp, which was an amazing 18.1 seconds long.